CW00864043

Tackateeners, Moanybikes, & Pennyannyos

Author: Mary Ray

Illustrator: Michèle Ray

jujapa
hansville
press
washington

Hardback ISBN-13: 978-1-952493-01-0
Paperback ISBN-13: 978-1-952493-99-7
Library of Congress Control Number: 2020913622

Illustrations and Cover image by: Michelle Ray
Photoshop gymnastics by: Jujapa Press

Published by:
Jujapa Press, LLC
PO Box 269
Hansville, Wa 98340

NOTE: The views, preferences and opinions expressed by the authors in these pages belong solely to the authors and do not necessarily reflect the views, preferences and opinions of Jujapa Press, LLC, or anyone other than the author.

PUBLISHER NOTE: It's been a delight to help bring this book to the reader. Tucked inside the original concept of kid's versions of the words they think they hear adults speak, is the reality that we all experience the world with our own personal version of hearing, seeing, smelling, touching and language. We share those experiences through words that sometimes miss the target, sometimes describe only part of the reality and, most assuredly, we all experience each word in our own unique way, especially when all we see is forest of ankles and knees.

To Marshweed

Acknowledgements:

Thank you, David Radman for awakening a long held dream, and to Marshall for inspiring that dream. To Michèle Ray for adding color and life to the project, and to my new found friend and publisher, Clark Parsons, for providing expert guidance to a novice.

Introduction:

The experience of watching a child learn language is thrilling, wondrous, and always amusing. This book is a look back at the words my son reinvented in his child's mind as he experienced the world around him. Some of these words are still used in our home today!

There is room on each page for you to document your child's creative translation of these everyday words. You will have a precious, written record of the funny translations your child comes up with while learning language, and you will also have a book to share for generations.

ALERT: There is a small rectangular shape on each illustration. Put on your detective hat ⌕ and try to guess what those shapes are for. The solution is explained at the bottom of the final picture-page of the book.

What in the word is a tackateener? Open the book, let's take a look.

Those are dada's ackses?

Your version:

Silly baby, those are **<u>glasses</u>**!

Uh oh, look! I spilled my dinner, better get the tackateener!

Your version:

Ha Ha, you goof,
it's a <u>vacuum cleaner!</u>

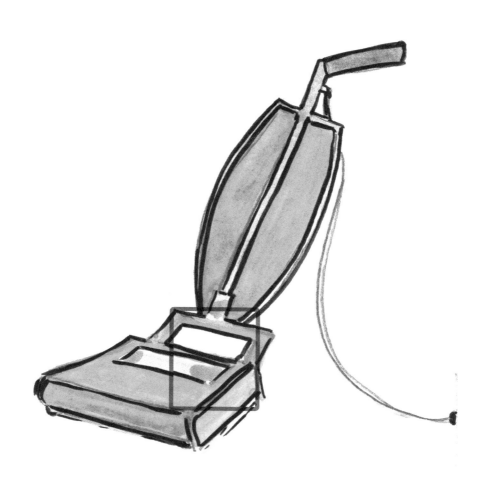

Breakfast is ready!

Look at that, you made
a great big patpat!

Your version:

You make me laugh,
until I shake,
but what I made
is a big <u>pancake</u>!

Out for a ride,
you on your trike,

look there, you said,

It's a Moanybike!

Your version:

Dada laughed from atop his bicycle,

funny fella, that's a <u>motorcycle</u>!

Look over there,
it's a honking goose!

I can't see mama,
you have to moose!

Your version:

If you say please,

then I'll approve,

but I think you'd like

to make me <u>move</u>!

See that, you said, "

up in the tree.

It's a baby mowkey!"

Your version:

You are as funny as can be,
but what I see is a little <u>monkey</u>!

Hurry hurry,
come on let's go,
I want to play

on grammas pennyannyo!

Your version:

Okay, okay, I'm coming, I know,
but that my son, is a <u>piano</u>!

Crash crash, bang boom,

Oh that, I think, is a big noise
from lighteling!

Your version:

It's loud and bright, and startling,

but what you saw was <u>lightning</u>!

It's party time,
today's the day,
we celebrate your
3rd birthday!
We have a cake, candles,
ice cream and spoons.

"But Mama, you forgot the
boons!"

Your version:

Oh no, not true, look up and see,
I didn't forget, it's three heart shaped
<u>balloons</u>!

I ate my lunch,
now may I have a tookie?

Your version:

Good job my son, you ate it all,

now you may have a <u>cookie</u>.

What do you want to do today?

"Mama, I just want to pay.

Your version:

Okay, after your nap,
then you may <u>play</u>.

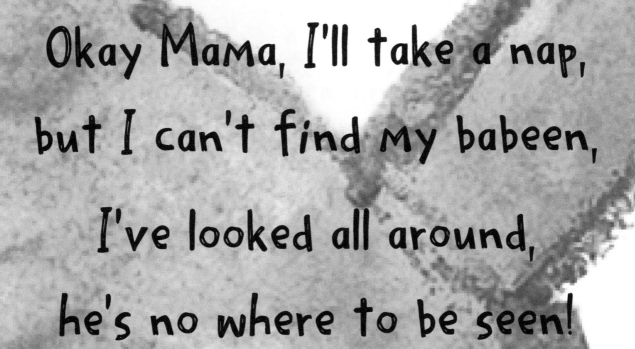

Okay Mama, I'll take a nap,
but I can't find my babeen,

I've looked all around,
he's no where to be seen!

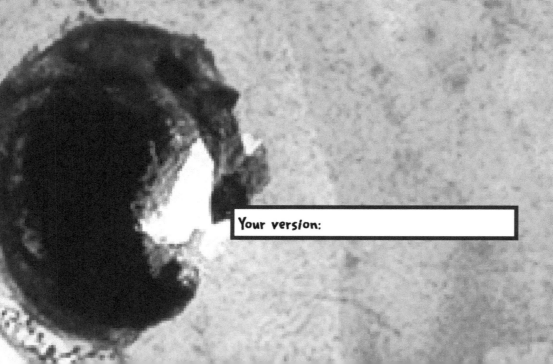

Your version:

It is your habit,
that when you sleep you
snuggle with your <u>bunny rabbit</u>.
I see him, he's over there,
hiding out behind your chair.

Here we go,
it's time for bed,
first take a bath,
and   what's next then?

I know, I know,
before I sleep,
I need to use
my teethen!

Your version:

You're right, and
though there is no rush, but
that is called a <u>toothbrush</u>!

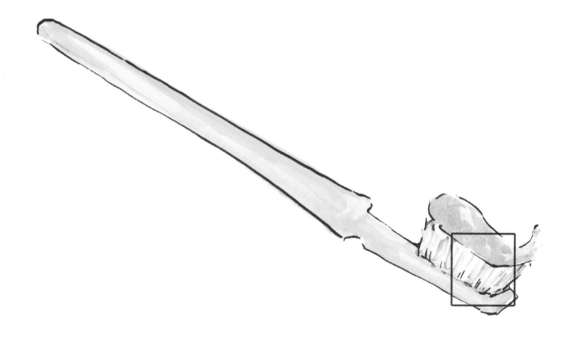

Solution:

The area in the small rectangles identifies what part of that image is enlarged many times and then used as the background on the previous page.

Your child's list of words!

Child's word	Adult word
1. backseball	basketball
2. tans	crayons
3. raildement	derailment (train)
4. _____	_____
5. _____	_____
6. _____	_____
7. _____	_____
8. _____	_____
9. _____	_____
10. _____	_____
11. _____	_____
12. _____	_____
13. _____	_____
14. _____	_____
15. _____	_____

Lightning Source UK Ltd.
Milton Keynes UK
UKHW050727061020
371049UK00004B/123